3,585 Miles To Be An American Girl

By Nury Crawford

Illustrations by Demitrius Bullock

http://1010publishing.wixsite.com/website

ISBN: 978-0-9993978-0-0
Printed in the United States of America.

Dedicated to my loving mother, the most beautiful woman this earth was blessed to hold, my angel. For her strength both in her love and courage, I will forever be grateful.

Dedicado a mi madre amorosa, la mujer más hermosa que esta tierra fue bendecida para celebrar, mi ángel. Por su fuerza tanto en su amor como en su coraje, estaré eternamente agradecida.

Acknowledgements

I truly could not have completed this book without the love and support of so many friends, both professional and personal. I know it is true when I hear people talk about the tribe they keep close. I know it is true when I hear people say, "Surround yourself with motivators, maximizers, cheerleaders for they will believe in you even when you don't believe in yourself."

A special shout out to Monica Garcia, school counselor extraordinaire, for helping me make sure I did not totally misinterpret the Spanish translations and for her constant support. I cannot forget to thank Charmaine Schneider, an awesome language arts teacher, who took the time to review the book to ensure editing was precise. I have to thank my sons for listening and enduring my commentary and growth along my journey as a novice author.

Of course, I cannot leave out Demitrius Bullock, the artist, who was able to put my story into pictures. His passion for the images he reflects via his art is immeasurable. Thanks for the countless hours of conversations and discussion.

Thank you to my uncle Moses and his wife for hosting us in our early arrival to the USA.

Thank you to my beloved parents, through perseverance and hard work, you ensured my success.

PERU

Lima
★

Mach
Picc

America here we come!

My name is Sofia. This is my family. We are Peruvians. We are from a country named Peru. It is a country in South America.

Mi nombre es Sofia. Esta es mi familia. Somos peruanos. Somos de un país llamado Perú. Es un país de Sudamérica.

We are immigrants. We are moving to the United States of America.

Somos inmigrantes. Nos mudamos a los Estados Unidos de América.

The flight is long. It lasts almost ten hours. We land in Indiana. Even the sky looks different.

El vuelo fue largo. Duró casi diez horas. Aterrizamos en Indiana. Incluso, el cielo parece diferente.

My uncle and aunt pick us up from the airport. Then my uncle drives us to their house. They live on a farm.

Mi tío y tía nos recogen del aeropuerto. Después, mi tío nos lleva a su casa. Ellos viven en una granja.

We meet a lot of people. They do not look like me. They do not speak Spanish. They speak English.

Nos encontramos con mucha gente. No se parecen a mí. Ellos no hablan español. Ellos hablan inglés.

My mom says I have to go to a new school, Mt. Healthy Elementary. I am so scared, but she tells me to be brave.

Mi mamá me dice que tengo que ir a una escuela nueva, la escuela primaria de Mt. Healthy. Estoy tan asustada, pero ella me dice que sea valiente.

School is different here. We do not have to wear uniforms. Students do not have to be quiet here.

Aqui, la escuela es diferente. No tenemos que usar uniformes. Los estudiantes no tienen que estar callados.

My little sister is scared too. She's crying. I just want to hug her.

Mi hermana pequeña también está asustada. Ella está llorando. Sólo quiero abrazarla.

When I get home, my mom tells me I am the bravest, smartest girl in the world.

Cuando llego a casa, mi mamá me dice que soy la niña más valiente, la más inteligente del mundo.

4.95
1.83
3.12

2) 37.79
- 13.54
24.2...

3) 19.68
- 3.43
16.25

4) 27.87
- 12.62
15.25

6.19
.55
.64

6) 17.6...
- 4.5
13.15

...9.93
...62.57
...7.3...

8) 48.29
- 21.65

25.2
21.7

10)

...287...

12) 834.4
- 127.9

Motion

One day in math class, we play a game. I go up to the board. The teacher tells me the math problem in Spanish. She has a dictionary. I'm happy I know how to solve it. It is easy!

Un dia en la clase de matemáticas, jugamos un juego. Voy al tablero. La profesora me dice el problema de matemáticas en español. Ella tiene un diccionario. Estoy feliz de saber cómo solucionarlo. ¡Es fácil!

My dad leaves for work before I wake up. He's a mechanic. He returns when I'm in bed. He is tired. In Peru, my dad worked in the airforce base, he taught classes on how to fix airplanes. He is so smart.

Mi papá se va a trabajar antes de despertarme. Él es un mecánico. Regresa cuando estoy en la cama. Está cansado. En Perú, mi papá trabajó en la base de la fuerza aérea y enseñó clases sobre cómo arreglar aviones. El es muy inteligente.

My mom babysits all day. She looks sad. She takes care of us. She is tired too.

Mi mamá cuida a bebes todo el día. Ella se ve triste. Ella cuida de nosotros. Ella también está cansada.

I will work hard every day to be the best that I can be. I am proud to be an American. I am proud to be from Peru. I am proud to be Hispanic. I am proud to be bilingual. I am proud to be a brown girl with long black hair. I am proud to have traveled 3,585 miles to be an American girl.

Voy a trabajar duro todos los días para ser lo mejor que puedo ser. Me siento orgullosa de ser Americana. Me siento orgullosa de ser de Perú. Me siento orgullosa de ser hispana. Me siento orgullosa de ser bilingüe. Me siento ser orgullosa ser una niña de piel morena con el pelo largo y negro. Me siento orgullosa haber viajado 3,585 millas para ser una niña Americana.

About the Author

Nury (Castillo) Crawford is originally from Peru, South America. She migrated to Columbus, Indiana at the age of ten along with her family. Her father, mother, sister and newborn baby brother all arrived to live with her uncle and aunt in their home; with nothing, but the luggage they brought with them. The first year, as it is for many children who migrate to America, was very challenging for the entire family. Many times children have to learn to deal with the challenges themselves at school since adults have their own benchmarks to meet. When Nury arrived, no one spoke Spanish at the school nor did she speak any English. ESOL classes were non-existent in 1979 at Mount Healthy Elementary. Her younger sister appeared to encounter a more difficult transition. Her brother was three months old when they arrived in American soil. Her father began working the following week. Both her parents enrolled in English courses, at the local community college, the following week, as well. Her mother would take the baby to class with her. By the end of the first year, her parents had enough money to buy a used car and move out of their relatives' home. They eventually moved to Florida. Nury completed her bachelor's degree, master's degree, got married, had her first son and began teaching by the age of 24.

She currently resides in metro Atlanta and has dedicated her life to the education of children. As the population changes, she has found yet another thread in common with many children and family migrating from Spanish speaking countries. She finds satisfaction helping all children find their strengths and self-confidence. Through the message of love, perseverance, and confidence she is a true believer in having the power of making a change.

About the Illustrator

Demitrius "Motion" Bullock, artist, illustrator, actor and now author, has illustrated 10 publications to date which includes 6 children's books and 4 book covers. He draws his inspiration from his family and notably his youngest son Bryce, who is the main character in his books.

Demitrius is a self taught artist from the Bronx, NY in multiple mediums. He was inspired by early street artists he witnessed as a child and his fascination with comic and graphic art led him to develop several of his own characters that have debuted at the Dover Comic Con in 2015.

He continues drawing and creating his own artwork and the building of his business Motion Illustrationz with his wife Michelle and son Bryce. Demitrius currently has his artwork on display as the resident artist of Artzscape Gallery, Wilmington, DE, and on his website www.demitrius-bullock.pixels.com.

Made in the USA
Columbia, SC
03 September 2020